£7.99

This annual belongs to:

Calvin

Age:

8

Favourite Looney Tune's character:

Bugs Bunny

WELCOME TO
LOONEY TUNES PRESENTS...
BUGS BUNNY
AND FRIENDS

ANNUAL 2012

Attack of the Killer Carrots

WB.231

Writer: Jack Enyart Penciller: Luis Sepúlveda Inker: Jorge Durán Letterer: Lorina Mapa

Continued on page 14

THE 'WRITE' STUFF!

HOW 'BOUT THIS CRAZY CARROT PEN - LOOKS GOOD ENOUGH TO EAT!

1 Draw a circle on some thin card. Divide it into quarters and cut them out. Roll one of the quarters into a cone shape around a pen. Snip the narrower end off, making sure the end of the pen sticks out.

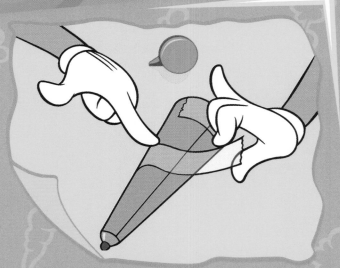

2 Secure the cardboard cone with sticky tape. Put some tape around the narrow end of the cone to hold the pen in place. Stick the other end down as well.

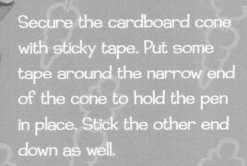

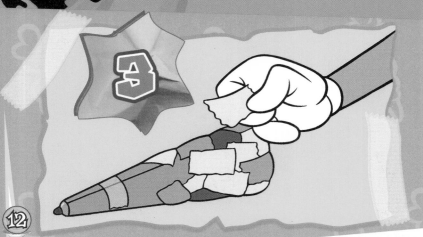

3 Cover the cardboard cone with three layers of paper maché. Make sure you put some on the join between the cardboard and the pen nib. Leave it to dry until it's rock hard.

4

Now decorate. Paint it bright orange. Add shredded tissue paper to the top to look like a real carrot!

Bugs Bunny

YOU WILL NEED!

card, pen, scissors, sticky tape, newspaper, PVA glue, paints, green tissue paper.

Continued from page 11

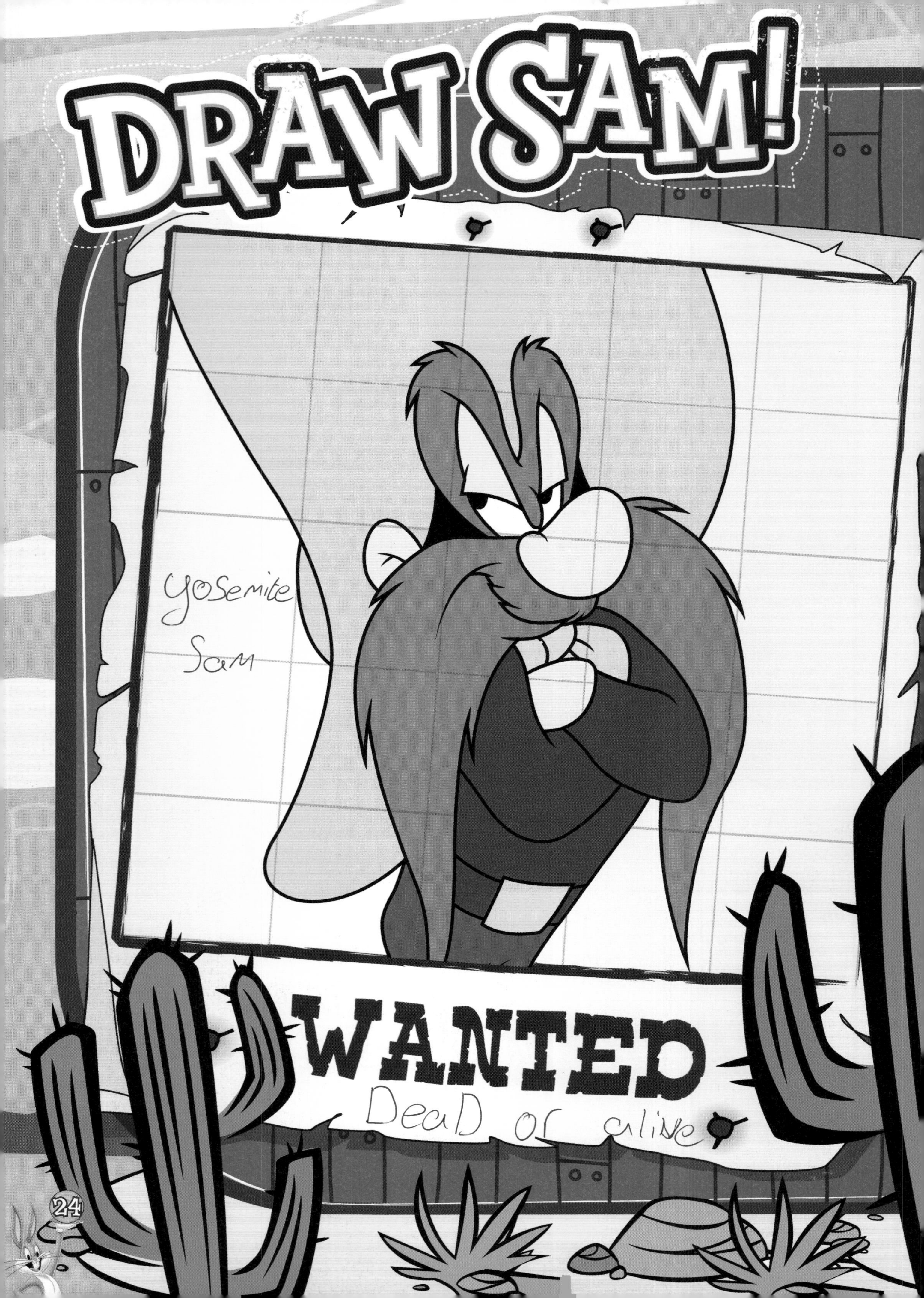
DRAW SAM!
Yosemite
Sam
WANTED
Dead or alive

Yosemite

Sam

WANTED

Dead or alive

25

THIS IS SO EXCITING! OUR VERY OWN **EXCHANGE STUDENT** FROM ANOTHER CULTURE!

TIMMY, JUST THINK OF THE FUN YOUR'LL HAVE WITH TAZLO--INTRODUCING HIM TO YOUR FRIENDS, PLAYING BASEBALL, TAKING HIM TO SCHOOL...

THERE'S SO MUCH WE CAN SHOW LITTLE TAZLO

TAZLO!

!@#$%^ TAZ HERE ^&$%~&(&^%$# PFFZTH!

CAN WE SHOW HIM HOW TO **SHAVE**?

PLEASURE TO MEET YOU TAZLO! WEKCOME TO OUR FAMILY!

MAYBE THEY DON'T SHAKE HANDS IN HIS COUNTRY?

IF THAT'S HELLO, I'D HATE TO SEE HOW THEY SAY **GOODBYE**.

AH... AH...

HON, WOULD IT BE MALIGNING HIS HERITAGE TO SUGGEST HE COVER HIS MOUTH WHEN HE SNEEZES?

QUICK THINKING, TAZ!

SEE, TIMMY! OTHER CULTURES HAVE FRESH, NATURAL INGENUITY!

SINCE YOU'RE SO LIKE, ADVANCED, TAZLO, CAN I HAVE SOME OF YOUR FRIES?

SMAK

NOW, TAZLO, ALL CIVILIZED SOCIETIES ARE BASED ON SHARING!

UH...NO THANKS.

ISN'T THAT SWEET! IN HIS COUNTRY, THAT MUST BE A DELICACY!

Continued on page 3

Fair 'n' Square!

Which squares are needed to complete the picture?

Continued from page 30

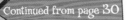

SIGN LANGUAGE!

Use the key below to help Taz work out what She-Devil has prepared for his lunch!

Chicken

Pineapple

and gravy

pie

A B C D E F G H I J K L M

N O P Q R S T U V W X Y Z

40

SPOT THE DIFFERENCE!

CAN YOU FIND THE SIX DIFFERENCES BETWEEN THESE TWO PICTURES?

41

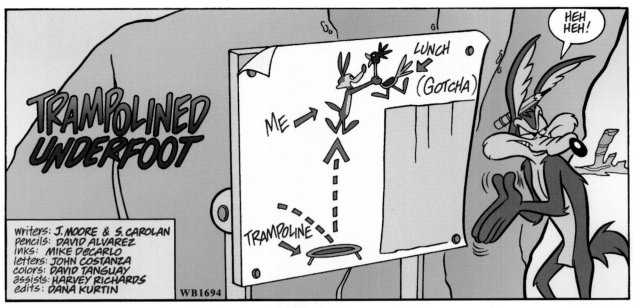

TRAMPOLINED UNDERFOOT

writers: J. MOORE & S. CAROLAN
pencils: DAVID ALVAREZ
inks: MIKE DeCARLO
letters: JOHN COSTANZA
colors: DAVID TANGUAY
assists: HARVEY RICHARDS
edits: DANA KURTIN

WB1694

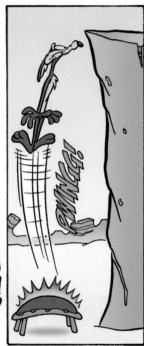

Granny's Fridge Cake!

Granny's having some friends over for afternoon tea! She thought you may like to learn how to make her special fridge cake! It's so simple and yummy, why not have a go!

You will need:

- 4 oz margarine
- 1tbsp golden syrup
- 8oz crushed biscuits
- 1 dessert spoon cocoa
- 1 dessert spoon fine sugar
- 2 dessert spoons drinking chocolate
- 100g plain chocolate

1 Crush the biscuits in a bowl and set aside.

2 Gently melt the butter, golden syrup, cocoa, drinking chocolate and sugar in a large pan. Once all the ingredients have melted, stir in the crushed biscuits and mix well.

3 Spoon the mixture into a small, greased backing tray or dish so that your cake is about 2 inches deep. If your dish is too big, only use part of it.

4 Next, ask an adult to help you melt the chocolate. The best way is to break the chocolate into pieces in a bowl and place the bowl in a pan of boiling water.

5 Once the chocolate is runny, pour over the top of your cake mixture. Put your cake in the fridge for at least an hour, or until the chocolate has set.

6 Cut the cake into squares and share with your friends or family! Enjoy!

THUD!!

OOOO, I HATE IT WHEN I'M RIGHT!!

SAYYY... YOUSE IS *RIGHT!* IT IS--IT *IS* A SOUND EFFECT!

I'D SAY I *TOLD YOU SO,* BUT I DON'T THINK MY MEDICAL PLAN WOULD COVER IT...!

ANYHOO, IF WE'RE DONE HERE, I'VE GOT ME A *LIVIN' DOLL* TO SWEEP OFF HER FEET!

HEY!

YOUSE DON'T SEEM TO UNNERSTAND WHAT I IS SAYIN', SO LET ME SPELL IT OUT FOR YOUSE.

NO, ALLOW ME. H-E-L-P!!!

QUEENIE *THUD'S* GIRLFRIEND. QUEENIE NO NEED *NEW* BOYFRIEND, SO YOUSE MUST GO--

WIND-A-WIND-A-WIND-A-WIND!

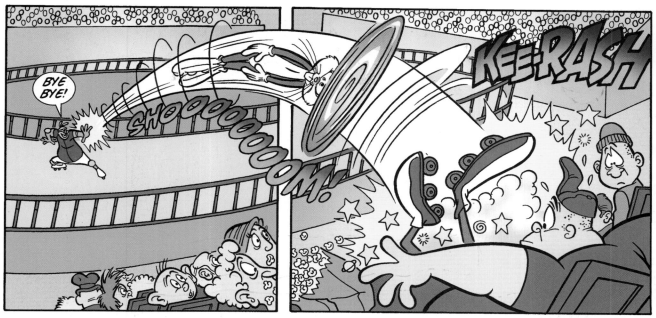

Continued on page 51

49

SNACK STOP!

T	I	H	N	I	F	F	U	M	L	P
G	O	M	E	L	E	T	T	E	R	W
E	K	A	C	A	Q	S	E	P	T	H
A	S	B	S	X	G	N	A	E	E	C
V	C	U	I	T	J	E	M	L	S	I
E	A	R	F	C	R	K	I	P	A	W
L	T	G	S	M	A	C	E	L	E	D
P	I	E	C	G	Y	I	W	G	S	N
P	E	R	W	A	E	H	M	A	G	A
A	Z	Z	I	P	S	C	H	I	P	S

Taz is feeling hungry so you'd better help him to find all of
the snacks hidden in the grid!

Eggs **Cake** ~~Pizza~~ ~~Apple~~ ~~Muffin~~
~~Chicken~~ ~~Toast~~
50 ~~Sandwich~~ Chips **Omelette** ~~Salad~~
~~Burger~~

Continued from page 49

OKAY, I GOT IT *WRONG* THE FIRST TIME. WHEN DEALING WITH BIG GALOOTS ON ROLLER SKATES, IT'S BEST TO SPEAK SOFTLY AND CARRY A *BIIIIG STICK!*

ACK!

FERSHOOOM!

"OR WAS THAT "SPEAK *BIGGLY* AND CARRY A *SOFT* STICK"...?

GOING INTO OUR *SIXTH* AND *FINAL* PERIOD, THE *WIPEOUTS* HAVE A *COMMANDING* 5832-POINT LEAD, WITH *THREE* MINUTES LEFT ON THE CLOCK!

WALLA WALLA 5837 — Altoona 5

IT'S NOW OR NEVER FOR THE *ARM-BREAKERS!* WILL THEY PULL VICTORY FROM THE JAWS OF DEFEAT, OR JUST LIE DOWN AND DIE LIKE THE *WIMPS* THEY ARE?

UH-OH! I SPOKE TOO SOON! THE *WIPEOUTS* ARE CATCHING UP TO HIM...

WHAT? WHERE? WHO?

YEP! POOR THUD DOESN'T HAVE A PRAYER AGAINST THIS SORT OF *ONSLAUGHT!* THE WIPEOUTS ARE USING EVERY WEAPON IN THEIR ARSENAL--

W-W-WEAPON?

--BASEBALL BATS, NUNCHUKS, BILLY CLUBS, TENNIS RACKETS, FRYING PANS, ASSAULT TANKS, LASER CANNONS, SURFACE-TO-AIR MISSILES...

WHIMPER!

YESSIR, NOT EVEN *THUD* CAN POSSIBLY SURVIVE THIS BLOCKING MANEUVER!

BUT WAIT! THUD'S MAKING HIS *BIG MOVE!*

AAIIIIEEE!!!

FAH-SHOOM

OOH, THAT'S GOTTA HURT! WELL, IT WASN'T PRETTY...

THUD!

...BUT THAT'S WHAT I CALL THE *SHOW STOPPER!* HEE HEE!

THAT'S ALL FOLKS!

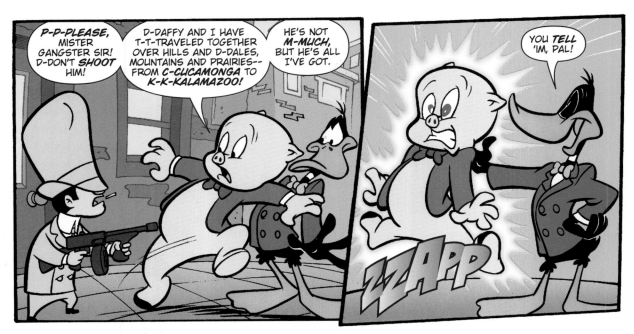

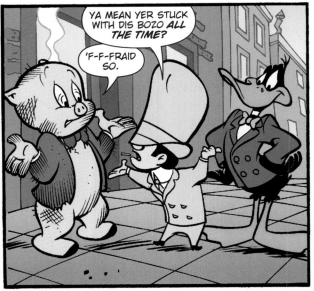